Uli Stein

0250
0000
STRAIGHT SHOOTER
0000
0000
STEIN

YOUR CAT CAUGHT A MOUSE MURRAY !!!
LOOKS LIKE HE WANTS A TREAT ?
NO. . .
. . . KETCHUP !

LET HIM STAY IN IF HE DOESN'T WANT TO GO OUT.
STEIN

DON'T TAKE IT PERSONALLY . . .
IT'S HER PLATE.

I'M HAVING HIM NEUTERED NEXT WEEK
REALLY ?
WHY NOT TAKE THE CAT TOO !

OK HERE'S YOUR MILKSHAKE ! BUT NEXT TIME YOU DIP A MOUSE IN IT YOU'RE OUT OF HERE !!
MILKBAR

YOU'RE ABOUT TO MAKE AN EXCITING NEW ACQUAINTANCE...

I KNOW, I KNOW . . . OTHER CATS SIT IN FRONT OF MOUSEHOLES ALL DAY TOO . . .
STILL . . . I'M A LITTLE WORRIED.

WHOSE CAT SWALLOWED THE SOAP ?

WHO STARTED THE RUMOUR THAT THIS IS 'MICHAEL JACKSON' ? ?

I'M NOT BEING RUDE, I JUST DON'T WANT HER TO GET STUCK.

CHRISTINE- I THINK THE KITTEN HAS PUT ON WEIGHT AGAIN...

JUST LIKE KIDS - THEY HATE TO TAKE MEDICINE UNTIL YOU PUT IT ON A SUGAR CUBE...

STEIN

THE CAT ATE THE WIND UP MOUSE AGAIN !
STEIN

GO HOME GUYS . . . SHE'S GOT A HEADACHE

STEIN

PISTACHIO
CHOCOLATE
STRAWBERRY
LEMON
(VANILLA MOUSE)
STEIN

WE'D GET A LOT MORE PEACE IF HE HAD HIS OWN TV.

STEIN

7
7
7

MR JOHNSON IS HERE WITH HIS CANARY, HE SAYS IT'S AN EMERGENCY.
OKAY, SHOW HIM IN. . .

THANK YOU FOR SEEING ME. . .

DON'T WORRY ABOUT HIS POKER FACE. . .WATCH HIS TAIL.

YOU WANT WHITE MICE FOR CHRISTMAS ?
ASK YOUR FATHER...
HMMM, HMMM...
PURR!

STEIN

HUPP!

STEIN

7

INSTEAD OF SPAYING HER THE VET FITTED A BIRTH CONTROL COIL, BUT I THINK IT'S TOO BIG . . .
THANK YOU, PLEASE TAKE A SEAT IN THE WAITING ROOM.

Z
KETCHUP
STEIN

OKAY LET'S GO BACK TO WHEN HE FIRST BIT THE POSTMAN ?
STEIN

MARTHA, GET HER
OUT OF HERE
WHILE WE PRACTICE !

SINCE SHE STARTED WATCHING COMMERCIALS,
SHE INSISTS ON PICKING HER OWN FOOD. . .

SHE'S NOT OURS. . .
SHE WAS ALREADY HERE WHEN WE MOVED IN.

ERWIN!!!... YOU WIPED YOUR FEET ON THE CAT AGAIN !
STEIN

OH, THAT ONE. . . IT ALMOST GOT AWAY.

MOTHER, LOOK, AN ANGEL !

I HAVEN'T DONE HIM IN YET,
'COS HE'S SO ENTERTAINING !
STEIN